Ghostly Fun

by ANN McGOVERN

Illustrated by Marvin Glass

SCHOLASTIC BOOK SERVICES

NEW YORK · TORONTO · LONDON · AUCKLAND · SYDNEY

Text copyright © 1970 by Ann McGovern. Illustrations copyright © 1970 by Scholastic Magazines, Inc. All rights reserved. Published by Scholastic Book Services, a division of Scholastic Magazines, Inc.

1st printing .... January 1970

Printed in the U.S.A.

Ghostly Giggles

Griselda Ghost invited all her friends to her midnight birthday party at the cemetery. What did she serve?

*I scream
Chocolate-chip spookies
Ice-ghoul lemonade
Birthday quake
Evaporated milk*

What do ghosts like to do at amusement parks?

Ride the roller-ghoster.

What haunting melody does a ghost like to sing?

"Oh, what a beautiful mourning!"

Who did the ghost take to the movies?

A ghost writer and his ghoul friend.

Why is a ghost haunting a cemetery like a worried man?

He has grave concerns.

A zombie who thought he was dying
Just could not seem to stop crying
  Until his friend said,
  "You're already quite dead,"
So the zombie's tears began drying.

What do ghosts like to eat at the beach?

Sand witches.

When is a human being like a ghost?

When he's a groan man.

GRANDMA GHOST: My! But Gus Ghost has grown! The last time I saw him, he was just a little shiver.

COUSIN CREEPY: Yes, he certainly gruesome.

GUS GHOST: My teacher doesn't believe anything I tell her.

COUSIN CREEPY: How do you know?

GUS GHOST: She says she can see right through me.

GUS GHOST: Can I have some horror-berry pie?

MAMA GHOST (*nodding*): If you'll promise to eat it without gobblin'!

COUSIN CREEPY: What can we do to keep Gus Ghost from standing on street corners?

GRANDMA GHOST: *Give him a chair and tell him to sit down.*

SWAMI THE MAGICIAN (*rushing out of restaurant*): That rabbit stew you served has made me sick!

WAITER (*looking after him*): Well, that's the first time a rabbit ever made a magician disappear.

SKELETON: It's going to rain today. I feel it in my bones.

> A skeleton known as Jack Sprat
> Can no longer sit where he sat.
> For when he was thin,
> He could sit on a pin,
> But now he is getting too fat.

What do you call a skeleton who doesn't have all his fingers on one hand?

Normal. His fingers are divided between his two hands.

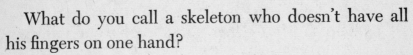

What monster has its eyes closest together?

The smallest monster.

What bird, found in a demon's cave, has wings but cannot fly?

A dead bird.

When is a black cat most likely to enter a house?

When the door is open.

How can you keep a werewolf from going mad on Halloween?

Shoot him in September.

Special Spooky Scramble

To find each spooky word unscramble each of these weird groups of letters:

REEIE   _ _ _ _ _ _

THOGS   _ _ _ _ _ _

CHWIT   _ _ _ _ _ _

MONDE   _ _ _ _ _ _

EVRAPIM   _ _ _ _ _ _ _ _

Answers on page 62.

Vampire Word Game

Vampires hide at dawn. Can you find 10 five-letter words hiding in V-A-M-P-I-R-E-S?

Answers on page 62.

The Four Witches

Here's the trick

Tell your friend there are four witches hidden in a deck of cards. His job: to find them.

Ask him to divide the deck into four piles and put them on the table as the picture shows.

He picks up the first pile. He takes three cards from the first pile and puts them down. He deals one card from the first pile onto each of the other three piles. Then he puts the remaining cards from the first pile on top of the three cards.

He picks up the second pile. He takes three cards from the second pile and puts them down. He deals one card from the second pile onto each of the other three piles. Then he replaces the cards from the second pile on top of the three cards.

He does the same thing with the third and fourth piles.

By this time, it looks as if the cards are thoroughly mixed up. So your friend will be doubly amazed when he turns up the top card on each pile — and uncovers the four witches (queens)!

Here's how

Before you amaze your friend, do this: Put the four queens on top of the deck. When your friend divides the deck into four piles, be sure that the pile with the four queens is the fourth pile.

Practice this trick alone before you mystify your friends with it.

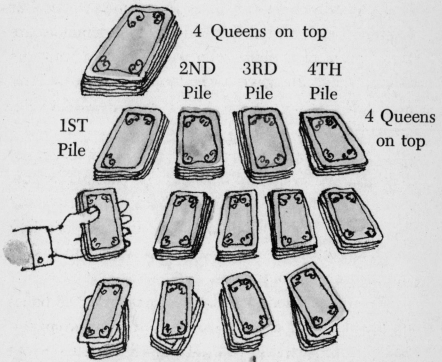

4 Queens on top

2ND Pile 3RD Pile 4TH Pile

1ST Pile

4 Queens on top

From first pile, deal off three cards, then deal one card onto each of the other three piles, then replace pile on the first three cards dealt from it. Do the same with second, third, and fourth piles.

Turn up top card of each pile.

THERE ARE THE FOUR WITCHES!

The Skeleton's Bones

Here's the trick

You probably know dominoes as a game to play. But for this trick, you tell a friend that the dominoes are the "bones" of a pirate who was forced to walk the plank. Why? He gave away too many secrets. And now the pirate is a skeleton, but he is still telling secrets.

Tell your friend to mix up the "bones" or dominoes. Ask him to arrange the bones in one continuous line, as the drawing shows, matching end to end.

As he is doing this, say: "The skeleton has told me a secret number." Write down the number, fold the paper, and put it aside.

When your friend has finished arranging the bones of the skeleton, ask him to open the folded paper. Say, "*Abracadabra!* The skeleton has given away another secret."

The numbers you wrote are the same numbers that are on either end of the line of "bones."

You can repeat this trick right away and as often as you wish, using a different pair of secret numbers each time.

Here's how

Before your friend begins to arrange the dominoes, take one and hide it in your pocket. Be sure it has two different numbers. The two numbers on this domino are the numbers you write down.

If you repeat the trick, exchange the domino that you first hid for a new one with two different numbers and write these two numbers down.

Your friend joins dominoes into a single chain, matching end to end as in the game. The two numbers at the end of chain match your prediction.

To make prediction you secretly take one domino. The numbers on it will be the numbers at the end of chain.

The Bewitched Band

Here's the trick

Say to a friend, "I hold in my hand a 3,000-year-old headband found on a skeleton. It seems to be bewitched."

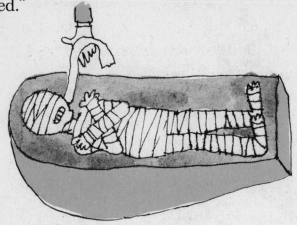

Tell your friend to cut the band the long way. Much to his surprise, he will find he has one long band, not two!

"Aha," you say. "This band is certainly bewitched. Let's try again."

Ask your friend to cut the band the long way again. This time, he will end up with two bands, but they will be mysteriously linked together!

Here's how

To make the band, take a strip of paper about one inch wide and twelve or more inches long. Before gluing the ends together, give one end a half-turn twist, as the drawing shows. (See next page)

Give strip
half twist
before
gluing
ends
together.

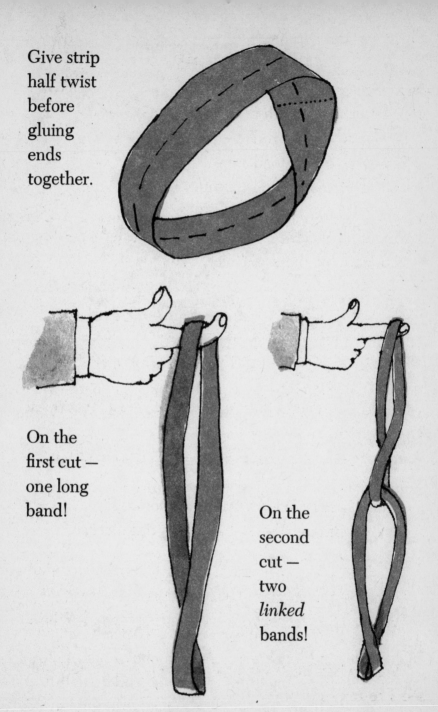

On the
first cut —
one long
band!

On the
second
cut —
two
linked
bands!

Horrible Ha-Ha's

On a cold wintry night in a blizzard
A skeleton dined with a wizard.
  The tea room they rode to
  Was fresh out of toad stew,
So they had to eat finely ground lizard.

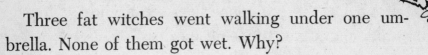

Three fat witches went walking under one umbrella. None of them got wet. Why?

It wasn't raining.

WANDA WITCH: I don't know what I'm going to do. My husband keeps a pet skunk, and the smell in the house is horrible.

WINNIE WITCH: That's easy to get rid of. Just open the window.

WANDA WITCH: What? And let all my bats fly out?

FIRST GHOST: Why aren't you working?
SECOND GHOST: I've lost my haunting license.

Mr. Ghost woke at midnight in a terrible temper. "Where's my supper?" he yelled at his wife.

"Where is my sheet? Where are my chains? Where are . . .?"

"Wait a minute," Mrs. Ghost pleaded. "Can't you see I've only got *three* hands?"

Three ghouls were trying to sleep in a narrow bed. After tossing and turning for hours, one ghoul said, "I give up. This bed is too crowded."

He took his pillow and lay down on the floor.

Soon one of the other ghouls called out, "Come back to bed. There's plenty of room now."

What is the difference between a ghost going up-stairs and a ghost looking upstairs?

One is stepping up the stairs, the other is staring up the steps.

A ghost who had lost his head
Got up on the wrong side of bed.
He had to go haunting
But his head he was wanting
So he took his friend's head instead.

When is a turkey not a turkey?

When he's a-gobblin'.

On which side of the old church is the haunted graveyard?

On the outside.

Diabolical Skit

It's fun to put on a skit. You'll need a few props for Dr. Diabolical's office — a telephone and a telescope for examining patients. (If you don't have a telescope, take an empty cardboard tube from a role of paper towels and paint it black.)

Make costumes that suit the characters.

For spooky sound effects, blow over an empty bottle or shake a jar of pebbles or nuts.

And here are plenty of jokes to liven your act.

A Daffy Day at Doctor Diabolical's Office

DR. DIABOLICAL (*on the telephone*): No, no, madam! Don't give your baby elephant milk!

VOICE (*offstage*): Why not? I'm his mother and I'm an elephant!

(*Dr. Diabolical hangs up.*)

(*Mrs. Witch runs in, frantic.*)

MRS. WITCH: Willy fell into the river. What is the first thing he should do?

DR. DIABOLICAL (*with an evil grin*): Get wet, of course.

MRS. WITCH: Willy can't sleep at night. What shall he do?

DR. DIABOLICAL: Tell him to sleep near the edge of the bed. He'll drop off more easily. And, as for you, I think you need a long rest.

MRS. WITCH: But you haven't even examined me. Why don't you look at my tongue?

DR. DIABOLICAL: I don't have to. I'm sure it could use a long rest too. Next patient, please!

(Mrs. Vampire enters, with her daughter Velma.)

MRS. VAMPIRE: I'm worried about Velma.

DR. DIABOLICAL: What seems to be the matter?

MRS. VAMPIRE: She's lost her appetite. Now she won't eat anybody.

VELMA VAMPIRE: And what's more, I can't do my homework.

DR. DIABOLICAL *(frowning)*: What does losing your appetite have to do with your homework?

VELMA VAMPIRE: How can I write on an empty stomach?

DR. DIABOLICAL: Have you tried writing on a piece of paper?

(Enter old Mr. Ghoul.)

MR. GHOUL: I've got a pain in my leg.

DR. DIABOLICAL: There's nothing I can give you for it. It's old age.

MR. GHOUL: But, doctor, the left leg is just as old as the right one and it doesn't hurt at all. And I've got another problem. I keep eating strawberries.

DR. DIABOLICAL: What's the matter with that? I eat strawberries every chance I get.

MR. GHOUL: Off the wallpaper?

(Daffy Demon enters, his clothes in rags.)

DAFFY DEMON: Help me! I just ate a stick of dynamite!

DR. DIABOLICAL: Why did you do that silly thing?

DAFFY DEMON: I wanted my hair to grow out in bangs.

DR. DIABOLICAL *(examining him)*: Hmmm. I see that you have little white things in your head that bite.

DAFFY DEMON *(in alarm)*: What are they, doctor?

DR. DIABOLICAL: Your teeth!

(Sam Skeleton comes in.)

SAM SKELETON: I'm so thin, doctor. What is the best way to get fat?

DR. DIABOLICAL: Go to the butcher shop! On your way out, tell my nurse to come in, please.

NURSE *(offstage)*: I can't come now, doctor.

DR. DIABOLICAL: Why not?

NURSE: I made myself some tea and I swallowed my teaspoon, so now I can't stir. Griselda Ghost is on her way in.

(Enter Griselda Ghost.)

GRISELDA GHOST: You must help me, doctor. I can't seem to remember anything I've just said.

DR. DIABOLICAL: That sounds serious. When did you first notice this problem?

GRISELDA GHOST: What problem?

(*Phone rings. Dr. Diabolical answers it.*)

DR. DIABOLICAL: Doctor speaking.

WATERY VOICE (*offstage*): Help me, doctor. A ghoul just bit off my arm!

DR. DIABOLICAL: Which one?

WATERY VOICE: How should I know? All eight of them look alike.

(*Doctor throws down the phone.*)

(*Horrible Monster enters.*)

HORRIBLE MONSTER: Quick! Give me something to cure hiccups.

(*Dr. Diabolical slaps him hard on the back.*)

HORRIBLE MONSTER: Why did you do that?

DR. DIABOLICAL (*pleased with himself*): Well, you don't have hiccups anymore, do you?

HORRIBLE MONSTER: I never did. It's my brother who has them. Give me something to scare him with!

DR. DIABOLICAL: Just smile at him.

(*Enter Winnie Witch.*)

WINNIE WITCH: Oh, I feel terrible.

DR. DIABOLICAL: What's the matter?

WINNIE WITCH: Thousands of invisible bugs are crawling all over me!

DR. DIABOLICAL (*grabbing his hat and running out*): Well, don't brush them off on me!

Hideous Ha-Ha's

The guide at the museum was showing Joe and Jill around.

"Over here," said the guide, pointing to a shelf, "is a rare book, written over four hundred years ago." Then he led them to a long covered box.

"And in here," he said, "is the man who wrote it."

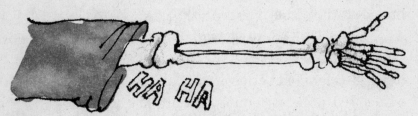

SILLY SKELETON: I laugh up my sleeve, because that's where my funnybone is.

A vampire who rarely vacations
Planned to visit a number of nations.
    When told with regrets
    That he couldn't bring pets,
He replied, "But my bats are relations!"

Mr. and Mrs. Vampire went to a hotel in the country for a vacation. A bellhop showed them to their room.

A sign on the door read: "Beware of the Thing." Bats flew around the dim yellow light. Broken shutters creaked and groaned. A table pitcher was filled with iced blood. Poisonous spiders were weaving their webs everywhere.

Mrs. Vampire said, "Oooh, this is just perfect."

"I thought you would like it," said the bellhop. "now if you should want anything, just scream!"

GRETA GREMLIN: Oh dear, I dropped a lighted match into a puddle.

GERTRUDE GREMLIN: What happened?

GRETA GREMLIN: It went out.

What do demons have that no one else has?

Baby demons.

What animal is a cannibal?

A cow. She eats her fodder.

How do you know that S is a scary letter?

It makes cream SCREAM.

What does every skeleton have that he can always count on?

His fingers.

What is alive and has only one foot?

A leg.

What bird looks most like the vulture?

The vulture's mate.

Why did Danny Demon wear a purple and green belt?

To keep his pants up.

Feel the Corpse

Tell your friends they are going to be "in touch" with a corpse! But don't tell them the grisly parts are really . . .

broken pretzels — for teeth
two freshly peeled onions — for eyes
two dried apricots — for ears
chalk — for fingers
mop head — for hair
pork and beans — for insides
carrot — for nose
wet sponge — for brains

Put these items on a tray and put a sheet over yourself for a ghost costume. Darken the room and tell your friends to sit around a table. Give them each a towel to cover their laps.

As each part of the corpse is mentioned, pass it around the table for your friends to feel. In your spookiest voice, read this poem:

If you must hold these, please don't fumble,
For if you do, my teeth will crumble.

(pretzels)

Ah, here are my long-lost eyes.
Hold them to your nose — surprise!

(onions)

Have you ever tasted ears,
Buried for a thousand years?

(apricots)

Oh, how *rigor mortis* lingers
In my dry and bony fingers!

(chalk)

Now my skull is cold and bare,
For it's you who holds my hair!

(mop head)

Oh woe is me, oh woe betide me —
This gloppy goo was once inside me!

(*pork and beans*)

Listen my friends, listen my foes.
You can't smell good without a nose.

(*carrot*)

Don't scream, don't faint and don't complain.
You have me all, for here's my brain!

(*wet sponge*)

(Exit with a ghostly cry, while your friends shiver.)

Ghastly Giggles

VERONICA VAMPIRE (*in the dining room of an ocean liner*): I'm starving.

WAITER: Would you care to see the menu?

VERONICA VAMPIRE: No, just bring me the passenger list.

What has four legs and feathers?

A featherbed.

What has four legs but can't walk?

A chair.

What else has four legs and can't walk?

Two pairs of pants.

What has four legs and flies?

A dead horse.

What else has four legs and flies?

Two birds.

What has neither flesh nor bone, but has four fingers and a thumb?

A glove.

Tonight, when the last light is gone
And you're almost too sleepy to yawn,
   Put your ear to the wall
   And you'll hear the Thing crawl,
But don't cry; it leaves before dawn.

Outwitting the Witch

Do you want to stage a terrorizing treasure hunt? Change your name to Wilmer (or Wilma) Wizard and outwit a wicked witch!

Read the following message to your friends (or make up your own):

YOU HAVE BEEN PUT UNDER THE EVIL SPELL OF A WICKED WITCH. YOU WILL BE TURNED INTO MICE AT MIDNIGHT UNLESS YOU CAN FIND THE CHARMS TO OUTWIT THE WITCH AND TURN HER INTO CHEWING GUM!

W. Wizard

Before the treasure hunt begins, collect the magic charms for outwitting the witch. Read the following three pages to learn where to hide them. And then ask a few friends to your house for some spooky fun!

You'll need:

a four-leaf clover (If you can't find one, draw one — it's just as lucky.)

a rabbit's foot (You can draw a rabbit's foot, too, if you have trouble catching a rabbit.)

bat's hair (a ball of wool or yarn)

toad's eyes (marbles or pebbles)

vampire's blood (a glass of tomato juice)

With each magic charm, place the clue for the charm you want your friends to find next. The first person to find the charm should wait until everyone has reached the spot. Then the next clue is read and everyone rushes off to look for the charm it describes.

Here's the first clue!

> TURN FOUR LEAVES OF A SCIENCE BOOK
> TO FIND WHAT WITCHES OVERLOOK.

Hide the four-leaf clover between pages 8 and 9 of your science book. Leave the book in plain sight on a table or chair. With the four-leaf clover, your friends will find the next clue:

> WITH A LITTLE LUCK, I HOPE
> YOU'LL FIND TOAD'S EYES. GO WASH WITH SOAP!

Put marbles or pebbles in the bathroom soap dish, with the next clue:

> FIND THE SHOE IN WHICH I'VE PUT
> A CHARM AND YOU'LL FIND LUCK AFOOT.
> ONCE YOU'VE FOUND IT, BETTER GRAB IT,
> OR YOU'LL LOSE IT TO A RABBIT.

Put the rabbit's foot in a shoe and hide it under the sofa. With the rabbit's foot, leave the next clue:

WHEN THE MOON IS BRIGHT AND FULL,
THE HAIR OF BATS IS MUCH LIKE WOOL.
IF YOU WOULD BE SAFE FROM HARM,
THE HAIR OF BATS MUST BE YOUR CHARM.
DON'T LOOK UP: LOOK DOWN INSTEAD,
UPON THE PLACE I LAY MY HEAD!

Put the wool on your pillow with the next clue:

WHEN IT'S CHILLED AND GETS QUITE COLD,
VAMPIRE'S BLOOD IS VERY NICE.
YOUR FINAL CLUE I'LL HERE UNFOLD.
YOU'LL FIND HIS BLOOD WHERE YOU FIND ICE.

Put glass of tomato juice and the next message from W. Wizard in the freezer of the refrigerator.

When everyone has reached the kitchen, read W. Wizard's message aloud.

YOU'VE FOUND THE CHARMS;
YOU'VE SOLVED THE CLUES.
THE WICKED WITCH KNOWS SHE MUST LOSE.
YOU'VE HEEDED WELL
MY GOOD ADVICE.
YOU'LL NOT BE TURNED TO LITTLE MICE.

WITH FOUR-LEAF CLOVER,
RABBIT'S FOOT,
A HEX UPON THE WITCH YOU'VE PUT.
ADD HAIR OF BAT
AND TOAD'S BRIGHT EYES.
THE WITCH IS IN FOR A SURPRISE.
ADD VAMPIRE'S BLOOD,
AND NOW YOU'RE DONE.
THE BATTLE WITH THE WITCH IS WON.

THE WIZARD'S WISE,
THE WITCH IS DUMB,
FOR LOOK WHAT SHE HAS NOW BECOME . . .
CHEWING GUM!

Give each of your friends a stick of gum.

Witches' Brew

FIRST WITCH: I just cast a spell on fleas.
SECOND WITCH: Does it kill them?
FIRST WITCH: No, but it makes them itch.

Wanda Witch decided to see
How the wizards made their tea.
They boiled some bats
And some tails from rats
Then gave her a cup for free.

Bill Sneed hired a witch to stand in front of his house every night.

Bill's wife was terrified at the sight of the ugly witch.

She said to Bill, "Why is that horrible witch in front of the house night after night?"

"To scare the elephants away," said Bill.

"That's silly," said his wife. "There are no elephants around here."

"See?" said Bill. "It works."

Three grown-up witches and one baby witch were flying around on their brooms one Halloween night.

"Aren't we three having a wonderful time?" Baby Witch said.

Why did he say three instead of four?

Baby witch was too young to count.

When is it polite for a witch to serve milk in a saucer?

When she is feeding her cat.

If a witch woke up in the middle of the night, What would she do for light?

Take a feather from a pillow. That's light enough.

When is a witch's cheek not a cheek?

When it's a little pale. (Pail, get it?)

A young man went to a witch to have his fortune told.

"I will answer two questions for you for five dollars," the witch said.

The young man paid the witch and said, "Don't you think five dollars is a lot of money for two questions?"

"Yes, it is," answered the witch. "Now what is your *second* question?"

The Past and the Future: Funtastic Fortunes

You don't need a crystal ball to tell fortunes. All you need is a deck of cards.

Ask a friend to shuffle the cards. Then lay out seven cards, face up in a row. These cards reveal the past.

Lay out a second row of seven cards. These cards foretell the future.

Study the chart to learn what each card represents. Until you become an expert fortune-teller, you'll probably want to keep the chart handy.

Try telling your own fortune first to get the hang of it.

SPADES	HEARTS	DIAMONDS	CLUBS
School	Family or Friends	Money	Sports or Hobbies
King: father		Seven: short trip	
Queen: mother		Six: surprising news	
Jack: teacher		Five: fight	
Ten: find something		Four: good luck	
Nine: lost something		Three: bad luck	
Eight: long journey		Two: love	
		Ace: health	

Suppose the seven cards that foretell the future turn out to be: King of Spades, Ten of Spades, Nine of Hearts, Three of Diamonds, Eight of Clubs, Five of Hearts, and the Jack of Diamonds . . .

The King of Spades tells you that your father will be asked to school. (That could be either good or bad.) The Ten of Spades means you will find something in school. (Your father?) The Nine of Hearts means that your best friend will lose something of yours. (Your report card?) The Eight of Clubs means you will take a long journey having to do with one of your hobbies. The Three of Diamonds means you will have bad luck with money. (You might lose a dime on your long journey.) And the Five of Hearts means a fight with your sister or brother. The Jack of Diamonds has something to do with money and your teacher. (Perhaps your teacher will suddenly become a millionaire, or she might ask you to bring some money to school for a class treat.)

When you tell your friend's fortune, keep it fun. Fortune telling is only for fun.

The Witch's Teeth

Here's the trick

Show three dice to a friend. Tell him they were once the teeth of a witch and still have magic powers.

Turn your back. Tell your friend to roll the dice and to add up the numbers showing on the tops of the three dice.

Then tell him to pick *one* up and to add the number on the *bottom* of it to his previous total.

Tell him to roll this one again. This time he adds the number showing on the *top* to his total.

Now turn around. Pick up the dice and hold them to your forehead. Then say: "The dice feel cold and clammy. The witch is using her power to tell me the answer." After a moment of looking mysterious, announce the correct figure.

Here's how

Before you pick up the dice, add the numbers show-ing on the tops of all three. Then add seven to your total for your answer. This trick works all the time!

Your friend rolls three dice and adds the numbers shown on their top faces. Then he picks up *one* die and adds the number showing on its bottom face. Then he rolls *this* die once again and adds the num-ber on its top face for a grand total. You turn around and with a little hocus-pocus announce correctly the total he reached. (Just add 7 to the total showing on the three top faces.)

The Galloping Ghost

Here's the trick

Say to a friend, "There's a galloping ghost who lives in the pockets of my pants. He gallops from one pocket to another."

Pull out the two front pockets of your pants to prove to your friend they are empty. Put the pockets back in. Then hold out your hands to show your friend that they are empty too.

Pick up a white handkerchief and say, "This is the galloping ghost. Watch him carefully."

Put the handkerchief into your right-hand pocket. Pull the pocket out again. It's empty — no "ghost"! Push the pocket back in.

Reach into your left pocket — and out comes the "ghost." Put the "ghost" back into your left pocket, and show your friends your hands are empty. Reach into your left pocket and pull it out again. This time it's empty.

Reach into your right pocket and pull out the "ghost." Push both of your pockets back in. Then place the "ghost" in your right pocket.

Snap your fingers, say "glibbety-glabbity-glanished." And, wonder of wonders, the "ghost" has vanished!

Here's how

Make sure you're wearing pants with pockets that can be pulled out. You'll need two small white handkerchiefs or cloths that look alike. In the inside upper corner of each of your pockets is a small space in which you can hide a tightly folded handkerchief which will remain hidden even when you pull out your pockets.

Before you begin the trick, tightly fold a handkerchief and hide it in the corner of your left pocket. As you do the trick, simply wad up the handkerchief and tuck it into the corner of the pocket from which you want the "ghost" to disappear. Then reach into the other pocket and produce the "ghost," holding it between two fingers so that it unfolds. At the end of the trick, leave one handkerchief tightly folded in the corner of each pocket.

At start of trick, second handkerchief is hidden in inside corner of left pocket.

Now to make "Ghost" gallop hide first handkerchief in inside corner of right pocket, then take handkerchief out of left pocket.

Now to make "Ghost" vanish, hide one handkerchief in each pocket and show pockets empty.

The Unhangable Hobgoblin

Here's the trick

Tell your friends this story of Jorge (say HORGAY) the Unhangable Hobgoblin:

A hobgoblin by the name of Jorge was sentenced to be hanged for playing tricks on the King. When Jorge learned that he would die by hanging, he only smiled and said, "I'm Jorge, the Unhangable Hobgoblin."

On the day of his execution, Jorge was still smiling and saying over and over: "I'm Jorge, the Unhangable Hobgoblin."

Even as the noose was placed over his neck and the ropes were tightening around his neck, Jorge was saying, "I'm Jorge, the Unhangable Hobgoblin." And sure enough — the ropes passed right through Jorge's neck. He jumped to the ground, unharmed, and ran safely out of the kingdom.

Tell your friends that Jorge has passed his magic secret to you and that you will demonstrate that a rope can pass through your waist as easily as it passed through Jorge's neck.

Hold up two cords, six feet long or longer. Pass the cords behind your back and bring the ends around in front of you. Tie an overhand knot in two of the ends, and tell two friends to stand on either side of you and to grasp the cords. Tell them to chant, "Jorge the Unhangable Hobgoblin," while you count to ten.

On the count of ten, your friends are to tug firmly on the cords. Lo and behold! They pass right through your waist!

You can make this trick more mysterious by pretending to grow nervous as you count toward ten.

Here's how

When you first show the cords, it looks as if you are holding them side by side. But actually, hidden in your hand, the two cords are doubled and joined together only by a loop of thread — just strong enough to hold until the cords are pulled taut. Wear a jacket, or your shirt outside your pants, as you perform the trick, so your friends won't be able to see the loops or the thread. When they pull on the cords, the thread breaks and it looks as if the cord has passed right through you!

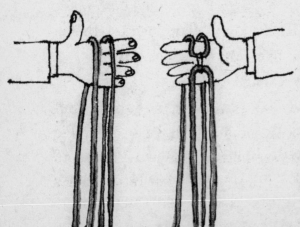

Your audience thinks it sees two ropes, side by side.

Actually, the ropes are doubled and held together by a loop of thread.

Pass the ropes around your waist, leaving them doubled, and bring the ends around in front of you. Tie an overhand knot in two ends. Tell two friends to grasp the ends. When they tug, the rope passes through you.

The Disappearing Demon

Here's the trick

Show a friend two pieces of paper fitted together as in the first picture below and tell him that the ten lines represent ten demons. The demons have been making too much mischief and everyone is trying to catch them. But, just as they're about to be caught, the demons pull some trickery. Move the lower half of the paper down and to the left, as in the second picture, and tell your friend to count the demons again. One of them has disappeared!

Here's how

Rule the lines carefully on a piece of paper and then cut the paper diagonally as shown by the dotted line in the first picture. The trick is an eye fooler, and the disappearance of the tenth "demon" is an optical illusion. When you move the lower half of the paper, the remaining lines become a little longer than they were in the original position. The "disappearing" tenth line was equal in length to the total added length of the remaining lines.

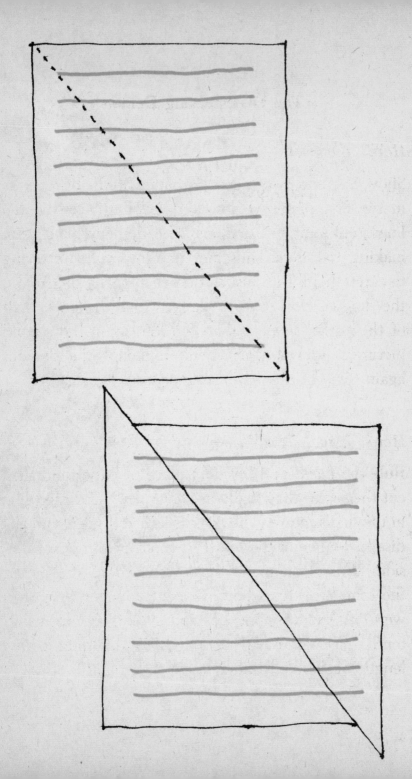

Gruesome Giggles

A witch who was ugly as sin
Went to work at the Pirate Inn.
  She would sweep up the rooms
  With her long-handled brooms,
And frighten the guests with her grin.

If a witch planted a puppy, what tree would come up?

A dogwood tree.

What do witches call little black cats?

Kittens.

When is a witch not a witch?

When she turns into her house.

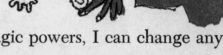

WITCH: With my magic powers, I can change any-thing.

SUSPICIOUS SAM: Like what?

WITCH: I can change this dime.

SUSPICIOUS SAM: I'd like to see that!

WITCH: Flibberty, gibberty, smee. Here's a nickel and five pennies, see?

44

Two witches were boasting of their magic powers.

FIRST WITCH: I can even make an animal drop from the clouds.

SECOND WITCH (*suspicious*): Which animal?

FIRST WITCH: Rain, dear.

Two witches were murmuring magic chants.

FIRST WITCH: Abracadabra. Hoky moky sloky pox.

SECOND WITCH: Nice day today.

FIRST WITCH: Hey, what kind of a chant is that?

SECOND WITCH: That's not a chant. I'm practicing a foreign language.

A goblin who lived on the moon
Decided he'd have to leave soon
   To avoid being caught
   By the strange astronaut
Who was coming the next day at noon.

MAMA GHOUL *(to Baby Ghoul)*: Are you HUN-GARY?

BABY GHOUL *(whimpering)*: Yes, SIAM.

MAMA GHOUL: I'll FIJI. Stop crying.

BABY GHOUL *(still whimpering)*: I want a slice of TURKEY, fried in GREECE.

MAMA GHOUL: If you'll stop your WALES, I'll give you SAMOA.

When do witches have eight feet?

When there are four of them.

What does the witch put off until tomorrow?

Her clothes, before she goes to bed.

A witch had five children and half of them were boys. How could that be?

The other half were boys too.

The Velvet Ribbon

Once there was a man who fell in love with a beautiful girl. And before the next full moon rose in the sky, they were wed.

To please her husband, the young wife wore a different gown each night. Sometimes she was dressed in yellow; other nights she wore red or blue or white. And she always wore a black velvet ribbon around her slender neck.

Day and night she wore that ribbon, and it was not long before her husband's curiosity got the better of him.

"Why do you always wear that ribbon?" he asked.

She smiled a strange smile and said not a word.

At last her husband got angry. And one night he shouted at his bride. "Take that ribbon off! I'm tired of looking at it."

"You will be sorry if I do," she replied. "So I won't."

Every morning at breakfast, the husband ordered his wife to remove the black velvet ribbon from around her neck. Every night at dinner he told her the same thing.

But every morning at breakfast and every night at dinner, all his wife would say was, "You'll be sorry if I do. So I won't."

A week passed. The husband no longer looked into his wife's eyes. He could only stare at that black velvet ribbon around her neck.

One night as his wife lay sleeping, he tiptoed to her sewing basket. He took out a pair of scissors.

Quickly and quietly, careful not to awaken her, he bent over his wife's bed   and

SNIP! went the scissors, and the velvet ribbon fell to the floor
                                      and

SNAP! off came her head. It rolled over to the floor in the moonlight, wailing tearfully:

"I . . . told . . . you . . . you'd . . . be . . . s-o-r-r-y!"

The Dream House

Night after night, Mr. Jones dreamed about an old gray house, standing in the middle of a dense forest. After a month of dreaming about this house, Mr. Jones felt he knew it better than his own.

One stormy night, as he was driving his car through the path in the woods to a distant town, he suddenly came upon a clearing. And in the middle of this clearing stood the house of his dreams! Shaking with excitement, he parked his car and ran to the front of the house. Trembling, he rang the rusty doorbell. Then he waited. And waited. After a while, a wrinkled old lady, dressed all in black, opened the door slowly.

"Pardon me, madam," Mr. Jones said. "Can you tell me if this house is for sale?"

"Yes it is," croaked the old lady, "but you wouldn't want to buy it." She began to close the door.

"But why?" asked Mr. Jones.

"Because it's haunted," replied the old lady, closing the door a little more.

"Haunted!" he said. "By whom?"

"By *you!*" said the old lady, slamming the door in his face.

Hair-Raising Ha-Ha's

The one-eyed monster went to the movie house. He said to the man at the ticket window, "Because of my one eye, I can only see half the movie. So you should let me in for half price."

"It will take you twice as long to see the whole movie," said the man, "so you'll have to pay double."

Why did Dim-Wit Demon go into the street with his bread and butter?

He was looking for a traffic jam.

Did Dim-Wit Demon find the traffic jam?

Yes. A truck came along and gave him a big jar.

What should a skeleton always do with his eyes?

Dot them.

A ghoul dug a grave six feet deep
And climbed in, preparing to sleep.
  But he heard someone sneeze,
  And, though weak in the knees,
He bounded back out in one leap.

If a ghoul ate her mother and father, what would that make her?

An orphan.

Why can't Gus Ghoul remember the last tooth he had pulled?

Because it went right out of his head.

FATHER: All right, Son, I give up. What *does* have three horns, one red eye, breathes fire, and creeps down the stairs.

DANNY: I don't know, Dad, but whatever it is, it's behind your chair!

A witch ate two fried eggs every morning for breakfast. She had no chickens and nobody ever gave her any eggs. She never bought, borrowed or begged eggs. How did she get them?

She picked the P's out of pegs, and ate what was left.

How can a witch make a pearl out of a pear?

Add an L to it.

What kind of umbrella does a witch carry on a rainy day?

A wet one.

What witch wears the largest black hat?

The one with the largest head.

With which hand should a witch stir her witch's brew?

With either. But it's better to stir it with a spoon.

MOTHER DEMON: If you were a good father, you'd take Danny Demon to the zoo.
FATHER DEMON: I should say not! If the zoo wants him, let them come and get him!

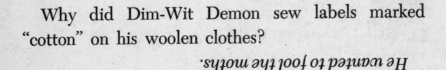

Why did Dim-Wit Demon sit on the roof?

He heard that the treats were on the house.

Why did Dim-Wit Demon sleep on the lamp?

He was a light sleeper.

Why did Dim-Wit Demon keep running around his bed?

He wanted to catch up on his sleep.

Why did Dim-Wit Demon sew labels marked "cotton" on his woolen clothes?

He wanted to fool the moths.

Why is this the last riddle in the book?

Because there aren't any more.

Ghosts and Witches Test

1. Name of a long dead pirate who haunted an inn?
   B _ _ _ _ _ _ _ _

2. Country where the witch lived who melted when water was thrown on her. _ _

3. Place where a boy ghost from Colonial times lived.
   D _ _ _ _ _ H _ _ _ _ _

4. The name of a terribly wicked Count of Transylvania? D _ _ _ _ _ _

5. What kind of creature was he? V _ _ _ _ _ _

6. The name of a tale about a witch who tried to get a girl to look in the oven? H _ _ _ _ _ and G _ _ _ _ _

7. A witch's favorite pet, or what they call a "familiar"? b _ _ _ _ c _ _

8. The night that spirits are supposed to walk?
   H _ _ _ _ _ _ _ _

9. What most witches ride on? b _ _ _ _ _

10. A magic number is t _ _ _ _.

11. When multiplied by itself it's n _ _ _.
    (The first rhymes with me, the second, with mine.)

12. A person under a witch's spell is b _ _ _ _ _ _ _ _.

Answers on page 62.

Tricky Teaser

Across

1. To cool a soda, add an ice _____.
5. What has four sides, and a top and a bottom?
6. To multiply a number by itself twice (3 x 3 x 3) is to _____ it.
7. A square lump of sugar is the shape of a _____.

Down (This is the tricky part; be sure to do "across" first!)

1. The captain of a ship may sail the seven _____.
2. When you eat, you ____ a knife, fork, and spoon.
3. Insects that sting are _____.
4. You should be able to do this puzzle with _____.

1	2	3	4
5			
6			
7			

Answers on page 62.

Witch Word Puzzles

I

Answers on page 63.

Print these words ACROSS:

1. The Thing! What is ___?
3. Last two letters of mysterious animal that witches often keep.
5. She flies on a broom.
7. You ___ candy corn on Halloween.

Print these words DOWN:

1. International Witches (*abbrev.*).
2. Before you make a hangman's noose, you must ___ a knot.
3. Put on a sheet and ___ like a ghost (*rhymes with fact*).
4. Terrifying hobgoblins (*abbrev.*).
6. Don't open your window, if you hear this sound (rhymes with rap).

II

Print these words ACROSS:

1. Thirteen witches minus twelve witches equals ____ witch.
4. It's not true that a werewolf goes ____ when there's a full moon (*rhymes with bad*).
5. How can a witch buy one of these and be sure that there is no chicken in it? She can buy a duck ____.
6. Nighttime Suntime Evils (*abbrev.*).

Print these words DOWN:

1. Something that happened which is looked upon as a sign of good or evil (*rhymes with Roman*).
2. Old, tired, worn-out horses.
3. The very brink of a cliff.

```
┌─────┬─────┬─────┐
│1    │2    │3    │
│     │     │     │
├─────┼─────┼─────┤
│4    │     │     │
│     │     │     │
├─────┼─────┼─────┤
│5    │     │     │
│     │     │     │
├─────┼─────┼─────┤
│6    │     │     │
│     │     │     │
└─────┴─────┴─────┘
```

Answers on page 63.

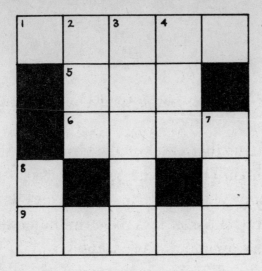

III

Print these words ACROSS:

1. Pulling a rabbit out of a hat seems like _____.
5. Real Living Monsters (*abbrev.*).
6. These are used to wash the floors.
8. Add one letter to change *pear* to *pearl*.
9. What is the opposite of *winner*?

Print these words DOWN:

2. Your _____ is connected to your shoulder (*rhymes with harm*).
3. Shines. A lighted pumpkin _____ in the dark.
4. A little demon or devil.
7. When you write a formal letter to a man, you write, "Dear _____."
8. Lost Lady (*abbrev.*).

Answers on page 63.

IV

Print these words ACROSS:

1. Put on a white sheet to look like this spooky character.

5. Because the book they borrowed is overdue, the witches now ____ for two days.

6. Openings. Demons sometimes dig ____ for cave homes.

Print these words DOWN:

2. The sound of an owl.

3. Who calls "hoot" and is said to be a wise bird?

4. A cat ____ in the dark.

Answers on page 64.

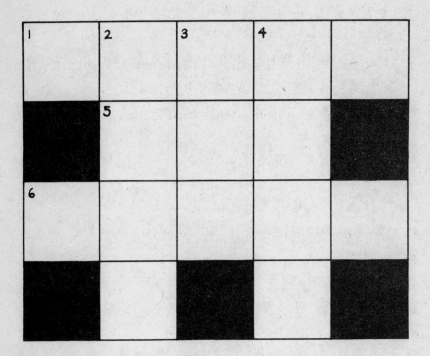

V

Print these words ACROSS:

2. A creature who weaves webs in haunted houses.
6. Gus Ghost ____ to haunt every day. Now he only goes haunting on Halloween.
7. This is where you find lions, bears, and tigers.
9. Can you draw a straight ____?
11. Otherwise. Run, or ____ you'll be caught by the THING!

Print these words DOWN:

1. Where you sleep, if the ghosts don't keep you awake.
3. The game you're working on now.
4. Icy Skeletons (*abbrev.*).
5. Evil spirits, or devils.
8. Even a witch can't mix this with water (*rhymes with boil*).
10. A fish that looks like a snake. Sometimes you say, "As slippery as an ____."

Answers on page 64.

Answers

Page 6 — *Special Spooky Scramble*
ghost
eerie   Magic-square word —
witch   SCARE
demon
vampire

Page 6 — *Vampire Word Game*

vamps	mares	reaps	reams
ramps	pares	pears	prams
spire	spare	spear	pimas
mires	raves	ripe	emirs

Page 52 — *Ghosts and Witches Test*

1. Blackbeard
2. Oz
3. Dibble Hollow
4. Dracula
5. Vampire
6. Hansel and Gretel
7. Black cat
8. Halloween
9. Brooms
10. Three
11. Nine
12. Bewitched

Page 53 — *Tricky Teaser*

You have probably figured out that each ACROSS word is C U B E. DOWN, you will have:

1. c c c c (seas)
2. u u u u (use)
3. b b b b (bees)
4. e e e e (ease)

I

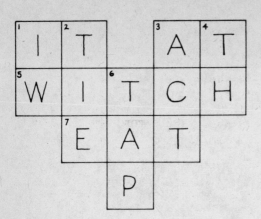

I¹	T²		A³	T⁴
W⁵	I	T⁶	C	H
	E⁷	A	T	
		P		

II

O¹	N²	E³
M⁴	A	D
E⁵	G	G
N⁶	S	E

III

M¹	A²	G³	I⁴	C
■	R⁵	L	M	■
■	M⁶	O	P	S⁷
L⁸	■	W	■	I
L⁹	O	S	E	R

IV

¹G	²H	³O	⁴S	T
	⁵O	W	E	
⁶H	O	L	E	S
	T		S	

V

				¹B	
²S	³P	⁴I	⁵D	E	R
	⁶U	S	E	D	
	Z		M		
	⁷Z	⁸O	O		
	⁹L	I	N	¹⁰E	
	¹¹E	L	S	E	
				L	